Introduction

At the ALLIANCE, we put people living with long term conditions, disabilities and unpaid carers at the heart of everything we do, from our partnership policy work to funding self management projects and developing new approaches in health and social care.

One of our key aims is to ensure that people's voices, expertise and rights drive policy and sit at the heart of design, delivery and improvement of support and services.

With Humans of Scotland we have taken that guiding principle and created another platform to represent those we work with. People - the 45% of people in Scotland living with one or more long term condition - deserve to be heard and this project spotlights their experiences and stories across Scotland's network of social media channels, websites and wider media.

The stories themselves are testament to the challenges faced by those living in circumstances that impact upon their health. Understanding this is not only crucial to our experience as human beings, but also important in a world where lived experience is becoming a crucial and necessary currency in shaping public policy.

In Scotland, the process of health and social care integration is about far more than financial or demographic pressures; it's about treating people as active citizens who contribute and enjoy the right to live high quality, independent lives in which they are in control.

If we are to tackle some of the most pressing issues in health and social care, we must listen to those at the sharp end, to those accessing support and services but also to those providing these services. We need to understand the challenges, as well as the triumphs, in an individual's journey so that we can provide better roadmaps for the future of the landscape in which we work.

It matters that we increase our understanding, that we listen and take on board people's realities.

Gathering the stories for Humans of Scotland has been a privilege. Every single person we have spoken with has been open and brave in relating their experiences, each with a desire to impart their unique take on life. This collection not only reflects the values of the ALLIANCE, it is a valuable insight into the lives of those who need to be heard in a world where so many can be marginalised.

Professor Ian Welsh OBE, Chief Executive, Health and Social Care Alliance Scotland

"Don't be satisfied with stories, how things have gone with others. Unfold your own myth" Rumi

"The most challenging thing for me is living with the daily knowledge that you have MND and it's a terminal issue. Despite everyone's best efforts there is still no cure, so when you have got MND you are told to sit in a corner and that's you till you disappear and die.

The game of rugby has taught me to fight for what you believe in, fight for yourself, challenge yourself, give yourself goals, realistic goals. I think my attitude has a lot to do with the rugby training. Sometimes admitting that you need a little bit of help can be tough. It's great to help people but can be difficult to be helped. That was a big change for me initially.

I played rugby in Melrose and Newcastle, I was lucky as I was very tall. I played for Scotland for maybe 10 years and then the British Lions tour of '97 and got a bit injured so came home. Never mind the rugby – I'm a games champion, I got to throw the welly the furthest. I'm still welly throwing champion.

Since I got diagnosed two and a half years ago, that's possibly the last time my consultant has spoken to me on a professional basis, as in a doctor to patient way, and that to me has been very frustrating. My battle at the moment is to try and make a

"The game of rugby has taught me to fight for what you believe in, fight for yourself, challenge yourself, give yourself goals, realistic goals"

change, try and give people living with MND – myself and others – a drug or something that will help us live longer and not have the horrific end of life that most people do.

I set up the My Name'5 Doddie Foundation and the support from the game of rugby and wider has just been so truly amazing. We have had about 700 functions in 20 months. We've been able to spend over 3 million pounds because it's money we have raised. That's £2.5 million on research and £500,000 on helping people with MND.

I never really let MND get in the way of things. I'm quite adamant about that, for example two months ago I went rally driving, just so I can say I could still do it.

I would say to people to enjoy family time and make memories. Live life. Right now I'm finding that I've never been invited to so many parties! Enjoy today and worry about tomorrow when it comes. "

Michael's Story

"It was lonely and extremely painful. The loneliness was caused because no one could understand my pain. All you want to do is escape from the pain. You have something you believe no one can relate to.

I went off the rails and sabotaged everything around me. Those four to five months were my darkest days.

I clung on to life an hour at a time and that's what I've done ever since. I've got a 2 ½ year old son. As bad as the pain was, I wanted to forge ahead.

The first time I went to a support group I was in tears the whole time. I don't even know if people could understand what I was saying but in some way it was cathartic.

When I found out I had complex PTSD I was relieved. I was denying I was ill for a long, long time. It was a freedom to own it. It's me and that's it. It's taken me 49 years to get to this point.

I write poetry, I go to support groups, they are absolutely my medicine. I

> "I went off the rails and sabotaged everything around me. Those four to five months were my darkest days"

volunteer with Brothers in Arms Scotland and run a support group and I help out with Stigma Free Lanarkshire.

I need some alone time. I need to do a bit of meditation, a bit of writing, it's blocking the outside world out cos sometimes I'm noise sensitive, I'm light sensitive. I have to find a balance.

I love waking up my son in the morning. It's the most beautiful moment of the day, just lifting him up and giving him a kiss. He's a beautiful boy.

I look forward to making a difference to people in the future, even just by telling my story, if they think 'if that guy can do it, I'll go and talk to somebody'. "

"I found a notebook that contained writing about the challenges, feelings and emotions I had within the first few months of having my baby. On opening the first page, I was transported to a time, not so long ago, where I was furious with my body for letting me down, for letting my baby down. I want to tell you what I wrote...

'My body is letting me down. At 8 months it has become physically impossible to hold her in my arms for more than 2 minutes at a time.

I worry about not being able to be a proper mum as I'm not able to physically keep up as 8 months of constant caring/being up/physical activity/being non-stop/the cycle of insomnia and knackerdness is really telling on my body and the combined psychological effect of 8 months of no/broken sleep is draining me in every way. I have thoughts every night in bed of what I'd love to be able to do with her, but I can't do these things.

I am aware of being physically weak and 'unable' for the first time in my life of living with Rheumatoid Arthritis.

"I picked up my defeated heart, dusted myself down and somewhere, from very deep within, found my usual defiance"

I can hardly get the sick drenched clothes off her or me, turn the dial on the shower or wash the sick off me, or dry myself, or get new clothes on, thanking god for my husband who is able to comfort her and clean up the mess. And I get angry at my body and myself for not being able just to get things done, or deal with my current agony.'

I remember that I had stopped writing because I was crying, with defeat in my heart. I had never felt defeat in my life before that moment.

What I can tell you though, is that I picked up my defeated heart, dusted myself down and somewhere, from very deep within, found my usual defiance, looked ahead and kept on going... "

Christine's Story

"I think maybe the greatest challenge was getting out in the world and being able to live like a sighted person, being able to do what everyone else can do. I lost my sight when I was five so I grew up not being able to see. I had to go to a boarding school and we had to become independent. From a very early age we had to do things for ourselves. I think that helped to give me confidence.

So the phone rang and I thought 'who's going to try to sell me something'? It was the Bank of Scotland to say that I had been selected as a possible torch bearer for the 2012 Olympics, but I had to keep it secret. Sure enough I got another phone call to say 'you're going to carry the torch'.

I got to feel the shape of the torch and we were shown how we would need to carry it. It's quite heavy and you have to hold it up.

"It was inclusive, I was just one other person. I wasn't any different to anybody else"

Because I was registered blind my daughter was allowed to walk with me when I was carrying the torch and she was six months pregnant at the time, so really there were three generations of the one family carrying the torch.

It was inclusive, I was just one other person. I wasn't any different to anybody else. The lady from Russia just held her torch to mine, lit it and the man from Alloa took the light from my torch and then he went on his way.

When it was the Forth Valley Sensory Centre's 10th anniversary we made a collage. On one of the squares, a lady helped me to make a replica of the torch, so that's on the wall here in the Sensory Centre."

"What makes me most happy is travelling and meeting different people. I seem to make friends more easily when I am abroad. I hope to travel to Slovenia this summer to meet a woman with whom I fell in love last year, but I will need to save money, which is difficult on benefits and a long-distance relationship is difficult.

As a teenager, I had to stay in the Adolescent Unit of Stratheden Hospital in Fife and was kept there for two and a half years. The longer I stayed there, the more and more depressed I became. At the age of 17, I wrote a book about my experiences there, entitled, 'The Madhouse of Love'.

Due to my education having been disrupted, I have never had a good job, although I was quite clever at school, and have had to survive by doing unskilled jobs, interspersed with periods of unemployment.

In 2006, I returned to Holland, where I had worked before, but things didn't work out and I ended up almost starving in a tent outside Amsterdam. I

"Relationships have been the only things that have given meaning to my life"

managed to get back to Edinburgh, where I became homeless. I stayed at the Salvation Army Hostel for about nine months before finding a flat from the council in sheltered housing.

My life has been very up and down recently, and, at times, I have been severely depressed. I am generally very isolated for most of the time and that has led to severe anxiety and depression. There have been times when I have been nearly suicidal.

Relationships have been the only things that have given meaning to my life, apart from artistic activities and travelling.

If I could achieve anything in life, it would be to be recognised as a writer and a musician.

The only thing that gives me hope for the future is the possibility that I still might be able form a relationship."

"I became a carer by stealth. As Mum and Dad got older, their fibs to the doctor became more significant, so I started to accompany them to GP appointments. Dad was happy to not have to drive as much, and that's how it began.

We got Powers of Attorney in place, and for a while, everything was fine. Then Dad was diagnosed with vascular dementia, and a couple of years later, so was Mum. I took strength from advice the GP gave me - 'You don't have to be the provider of care, but you do have to be the facilitator of care'. Meaning, prepare to knock on doors, call, research, call again, know your rights and keep asking for support. 'Facilitator'. I liked that title. But even that took a toll and takes time. I was made redundant, and to cut a long story short...et voila, an unpaid carer.

Your needs start to diminish in importance. Your calendar has appointments, but not for you. You stop making arrangements with friends, because you cancel so often, it's just another source of stress. Your home becomes a place of work for district nurses and carers, who would

"Your needs start to diminish in importance. Your calendar has appointments, but not for you"

walk into our home without knocking. I even made a sign, stuck it to the front door - 'Please ring bell before coming in', but it would be ignored.

I've seen acute kindness, and thoughtless cruelty. Now I have an intolerance of time wasters and meanness, but sometimes I'm laid back to the point of numbness. Thankfully I have good support from friends, my brother and his wife. My nephew and nieces are a joy. My dog is my sanity.

I've always been pretty resilient, but it's been a tough few years. Mum died a few weeks ago, my sister and my dad have died, too. During this time, I became a trustee of Dementia Friendly Prestwick, because I realised not everyone has someone to champion their needs. "

"Placement day is approaching, the day we go out to learn and be a part of this wonderful career we have set our minds to. Am I good enough?

I am there, I'm stood with all the nurses, some are tired, some are bouncy and full of life and some just look at me, it's another student they are thinking, will she keep up, she has no clue about this job, and I am thinking they are thinking about me and is she good enough?

I am introduced to patients, people. I walk in full of smiles because I want them to like me. I note that not many smiled back, but I'm still in that moment, me thinking do they like me, am I good enough?

Then there's time to get to know these patients, these people, humans just like me, I hear their stories and they tell me about this life they have, this life I did not see when I first walked in.

One patient is telling me proudly about their marriage of 60 years and I ask will they be visiting today, I can almost see their heartbreak in the expression

"I realise then this is about them, they are the reason I got up this morning, they are the reason I have chosen to be here"

in their face and tears in their eyes because no it's not possible because they also are in another building like this one with their memory slipping away and unable to remember the life they had together.

I realise then this is about them, they are the reason I got up this morning, they are the reason I have chosen to be here, I can walk in and out of this building, I am able to still make my memories, I have choice.

It's not about me or if I'm good enough, it's about that person sitting in that bed or chair. I don't need a smile back, I need them to know I want to be there because now I know it's not about if I think I am good enough, now I know I will do everything I can to make sure I am good enough for them. "

" I am a long-term survivor of disability and health conditions. I was born deaf with a severe speech impairment, this improved when I got my first hearing aid at University and it enabled me to distinguish words and sound.

I was diagnosed with multiple long- term conditions including severe depression many years ago. While all this was going on, I was a lone carer of 4 young children. This was an uphill struggle.

In 2012, I was diagnosed with diabetes and Retinitis Pigmentosa commonly known as 'Ushers Syndrome' which affects both hearing and sight. Because of this condition, I will never be able to drive or navigate unfamiliar places in the dark without help. Luckily, I got support through Access to Work for special equipment in order to stay in my job. My employer was great in making reasonable adjustments.

I have always gone that extra mile to make sure my disabilities are not a barrier to what I want to achieve as a professional, an employee, as a mother and as a human being. I've never let disability be an obstacle in my way.

Ageing with long term health conditions and disability is no mean feat. I look young but my

"Surviving and living with long term conditions is challenging, don't let anybody tell you it is easy"

body feels ninety. I tell myself to keep going whatever the problem is. Surviving and living with long term conditions is challenging, don't let anybody tell you it is easy. It is not. To me each day is different.

What works for me is the ability to listen to how my body feels and what I can do to address those challenges and seek support. Self-care and listening to your body is, to me, a fundamental core part of survival. I get a lot of support from my peers and my family. Good and balanced relationships between health care professionals and service users is very vital.

My children have in many ways inspired me to live this fight and stay alive with long term health conditions. I have had a very supportive employer who understands my good and bad days. To any anyone out there, please don't let the condition keep you down, it's all about keeping hope alive and the desire to be who you are even when your health and disability may pull you back sometimes. "

"On the surface it looks like I have it all together. I have good friends, two loving parents who are still together; I had a good education, a straight A school pupil, attended a top university and graduated with a first class degree. But I also suffer with often crippling anxiety.

I've always wanted to do things 'right'; my parents and teachers call me a perfectionist. I was a high achiever from a young age and continued to do well through school and university.

But around age 15 I started having panic attacks. My whole body would shake; I would hyperventilate until I couldn't see anymore. My hands and arms would tingle and I'd feel like I was going to throw up or pass out. No one could understand it – what did I have to be anxious about?

I couldn't answer them. The truth is, I could smile and laugh with friends but then come home and be a mess. I could force myself to go to lectures because it would stress me out more if I didn't go. I would hand in my essays on time because the fear of failing or getting marks deducted terrified me.

I could do a pretty good job of pretending

"I could do a pretty good job of pretending everything was fine, but no one saw the part of me crying my eyes out"

everything was fine, but no one saw the part of me crying my eyes out saying 'I can't do this', or spending every morning crouched over the toilet throwing up because my stomach was doing somersaults or calling my mum from work begging her to pick me up because it was all too much and I needed to come home.

I remember telling someone once I had anxiety and they replied with a shocked expression, 'Really? You? I never would have guessed, you seem totally together'.

When you can function relatively normally and go out with friends and go to work and university, no one suspects a thing. That's the funny thing about anxiety and mental illness – it can affect anyone at any time. So please, do me a favour and go out and check up on your friends who look like they've 'got it all together', because chances are, they probably don't – not all the time. But for me, through therapy I've learned that's okay. We're human and no one can be perfect 100% of the time. "

"It was 1956, I was eight years old, we lived in a top floor tenement flat in Townhead, Glasgow: It was dark, my brother and I were still out playing with our pals, the streets, and tenement closes and stairs were all dimly lit with gas lighting. I was running through my close, I stopped: there was a man standing in the shadow; I froze as he grabbed me taking me further into the dark; doing things I didn't understand: I had never experienced fear-terror until that night. I finally managed to let out a scream so loud he let me go, I ran back into the front close, my brother Jim and some pals were there, all I can remember saying over and over again, 'a man, a man'.

The next thing I remember was my dad coming into my bedroom and taking me into the hall, two policemen were there, they asked me some questions. That was the last time anyone spoke to me about it.

I was quite a bright child up until that night, I then struggled in class with poor concentration and continual flash backs, I hated going to bed and the nightmares/terrors were horrific, I still

"The many times I hit rock bottom with depression and anxiety I managed to write in a way that helped to release the pain"

get them. I've just undergone 3 years of therapy with a fantastic counsellor, if only I had this therapy when I was a child, my life could have been so much easier.

I'm 71 in June, how did I cope all those years? I was gifted with a great imagination; I could transport myself into places of joy and safety and write about it. The many times I hit rock bottom with depression and anxiety I managed to write in a way that helped to release the pain.

(Disassociation) is the bubble I've lived my life in. The evil that was waiting that night, wasn't waiting to get me, he was waiting on any child he could get; I am after all these years glad it was me and not my brother or anyone else; I was strong enough to get away from him, and strong enough to survive. "

"It was like, tonight we're going to shave mum's hair off. But things seem like a pure distant memory now.

My dad had passed away the year before. One thing led up to another. I was in a bath and I just felt a lump. I waited ages for the appointment. My doctor was like, you're only 27. They did a mammogram, and nothing came up, then they did an ultrasound. Then they did a biopsy, it was all on the same day. That was the Tuesday I think, then the following Tuesday I had the surgery. They said it was the most aggressive type, so I had to get it out.

It'll be ten years this year from when I found the lump. I always felt like right, I'm going to do this, I'm going to go back to work I'm going to get the kids organised, we've got things to plan we've got holidays to go. We've always got plans.

Worry is a killer. Every day I'm like I'm not going to stress about this, I'm not

"Wee things like that when you think everything looks all good on the outside but you're struggling on the inside"

going to worry about that. The small things don't matter. You pick your fights.

Some days, I do have bad days. I've got a lot of short-term memory issues. I struggle a lot with that. I've got nerve damage in my hands and my feet. Some days I'll be like what day is it? Wee things like that when you think everything looks all good on the outside but you're struggling on the inside.

My faith and my family, above everything else, that is it. I met him three years ago. We spend a lot of time together. He's a great person. We're moving forward. "

"I was going through a trauma and my family was breaking apart. I was introduced to heroin. The first time I tried it I was injecting it and it was an overwhelming feeling of bliss. It wore off and I had to take more. It got to the stage I was taking it to feel normal – I wasn't getting stoned. I needed more and more just so I could function like a human being.

It got to the desperate stage where it was either suicide or trying to get help. I went to the doctor and he sent me to the methadone clinic. He told me I'd be on it for the rest of my life. I believed him. The methadone took away the withdrawals, it basically saved my life.

I got not well, and I was taken into hospital and I was told I had Hep C. I realised I didn't want to die without fulfilling my potential and getting recovery. I was taken to Addaction. I grabbed onto every bit of knowledge. I realised I could get recovery and I could make changes to my life. I needed to find purpose and I found purpose in recovery.

It took me two years to come off the methadone, I was on it for ten years. I gave myself hope. One of the fears is relapse. I had to put things in place to give myself the best chance, so I got involved in building the

"It got to the desperate stage where it was either suicide or trying to get help"

recovery community. I beat the Hep C. I started building a life for myself.

When I came off methadone, I heard horror stories about withdrawal. But it didn't happen. I wanted to tell everybody that it was possible, and it isn't a life sentence being on methadone.

I realised I was able to speak out about recovery. I had a really strong message. I've been a volunteer for six years and I've been able to help people.

I saw a change needed to be made in society regarding stigma and misconceptions about addiction so I've actually made a huge contribution along with other volunteers by promoting recovery in the media.

You can change your life, no matter the obstacles or the barriers, or how much despair you're in or how much you've given up on yourself, or how much the world's given up on you. You can change and be a productive member of society. "

" I was a nurse for forty years. It wasn't until one morning when I was getting ready for my work, it was a back shift that day, I couldn't breathe. I thought, 'that's funny, not being able to breathe like this'.

I put it down to weight, so I just continued working and getting breathless. I went off sick. I went for the breathing test and that's what came up, severe Chronic Obstructive Pulmonary Disease. So, we went down the line of ill-health and that's how I took my retirement.

If it was just a cold or it had been my weight I would have stayed on. But because of my breathing I said I can't do this job anymore.

If it's too hot, it's a killer. If it's too cold, it's a killer. My heart failure doesn't

"I was getting ready for my work, it was a back shift that day, I couldn't breathe"

help either because you get breathless with that too.

It used to be terrible, it reduces your mobility. But now I'm a lot better, I can walk up the hill and down the hill. I think it's my weight, losing the weight. What a difference it's made. I do have my off days when I do have problems with my breath.

The singing for breathing group is a good idea, it does help. I love it. You're meeting other people that've got the same problems as yourself. We're all in the same boat. "

"Epilepsy takes over someone's life, takes over social circles, takes over their friendships. You're taking medication which causes severe side effects, that gets you down.

I was having too many seizures and had to leave university and had a bad case of depression. I was enjoying university, but I was injuring myself badly, dislocating my shoulders, breaking bones. I was in my flat myself. I was getting no support at all. I had a couple of suicide attempts as well. I didn't want to live.

Everything was so bad. I didn't have friends about me and people like family members were so stand offish and didn't understand too much about epilepsy and were being judgemental about it.

The toughest thing has been injuries, having to go through the whole hospital process, having to have a shoulder replacement, having facial injuries, injuries to my head, that's the worst really.

I ended up in hospital a lot. Being a young man as well and having to have a community alarm in my house, having to have bed sensors, having to have a wet room put in for

"Going from not having confidence to having amazing confidence is such a big thing"

my safety and having to have your bath taken out, not allowed to cook. I managed to nearly burn down a house three times.

I got involved with Epilepsy Futures which was a health and wellbeing project with Epilepsy Connexions. I went and I was an absolute nervous wreck, I literally crawled in the door, but it is the best thing I've ever done. It was meeting friends in the same situation. They were there to change their lives.

Now I'm a volunteer, I'm helping people. I want to raise awareness of epilepsy and mental health. People don't understand about both conditions and about how they're related as well.

I'm doing absolutely fantastic and I never, ever thought this would be the case. I'm just at a place where I want to be. Going from not having confidence to having amazing confidence is such a big thing. I wouldn't even go out the door. But I'm not scared anymore. I don't have the same fear. "

Raven's Story

"I have an invisible disability. The trouble is that on a good day I look fine but the next day I could be in my wheelchair. For this reason I get judged a lot and have to tell people that I am not a benefit cheat. I feel I am always leaving the house having to be prepared to prove my illness is real to strangers.

Using the blue badge is one of the most important things as it allows me to get out and try to be normal by joining my friends to go shopping.

"On a good day I look fine but the next day I could be in my wheelchair"

However, the looks and questions I get when people see I am parked in a disabled spot and look ok, it can ruin my day and make me feel so bad for using something that I need.

I have put on a limp before just so I don't get asked 500 questions about where I am parked. "

"I'm in supported accommodation at the moment. I'd let myself go with alcohol which I thought wasn't a problem until the last stages.

I took a seizure. Between my sister in law's house and the hospital I'd passed away. They resuscitated me. I stayed in for 13 weeks. I had pneumonia, TB and, I didn't know, I had Alcohol Related Brain Damage (ARBD).

I was disorientated, I didn't know the place I'd grown up in. I couldn't recognise the road. I was looking at the buildings and it was as if I was in New York, cos I thought I'd never seen these big buildings. I didn't know how to get down the road or up the road.

We got support from Addaction and the ARBD team at Penumbra. They explained that the brain, a part of it had been wiped clean and that's why I was disorientated and things.

I started building up, going to things. Being abstinent, eating better food. The brain started learning things. I was going to cooking class and doing other courses.

I got the opportunity to move into supported accommodation. I thought 'I would die for

"There's help there and you can get better. A wee bit of guidance, a wee bit of support from the right people and you can do it"

this', I just burst out greeting. For weeks and weeks after I was going 'when are they taking this off me?'

My brother died of a massive heart attack. We went to see him in the mortuary, and I kissed him, and I went 'I promise you I'll never drink again'.

Now, it's the best I've lived all my life, in the last nine years since I got my wee house. I'm doing my voluntary work, I'm doing peer support work, I'm looking after myself.

There's help there and you can get better. A wee bit of guidance, a wee bit of support from the right people and you can do it. I've achieved so much.

You'll never be back where you were, but you can still live a brilliant life. Everything I do now is enjoyable. I don't need anything. Just laughter. "

"As a young child I felt totally isolated, some may have said I was unsociable. I was a scared young soul who'd spend most of his time in his bedroom playing with Lego, it was the only way to feel at peace with myself.

I felt different from other children around me. Even as I began to learn a bit about my diagnoses of Asperger's Syndrome it didn't help, life was more challenging.

ASD not only impacted on my learning, my mental health suffered in Primary. The way I was treated, bullied by other children, staff who didn't understand me, or what I needed to help me, barriers everywhere. Ultimately, I lost six months of education. No school wanted me until John Simmons offered me a place in Castlehill Language Unit. A place where I was understood and I could learn and laugh again.

My path into fitness and sport, first came through Saturday morning special needs swimming lessons with Glasgow Life. I think my fascination with water and believing I was truly amphibious really helped my self-confidence.

"I felt different from other children around me"

Ski lessons came next. One week Ed from Disability Snowsport UK came along. The specialist instructor got the ASD kid, for he understood my challenges. Eventually taking me onto ski Cairngorm mountain.

With the help of Amanda, my teacher from Castlehill, Mr. Kerr at Abercorn, my ever-encouraging mother and my friend Janice Eaglesham I took up running at Red Star Athletics, sprinting being my event. I've been lucky enough to represent Team Scotland West at two National Special Olympics Games and work with my mother on my fitness.

As the first young ambassador for ILF Scotland Transition Fund I've been given opportunities to grow, I am listened to, able to reach out to other young people which is very important to me. I hope other young people will be inspired to give new things a go. If you're reading this believe in yourself and you can do it. "

" I never intended on being a stay at home mum. I had always planned on returning to my job part-time after our second baby was born, as I had following the birth of our first baby. This was before I realised that the decision of whether to return to work or stay home might not be one I would get to make of my own volition. We were living in Australia when our beautiful baby girl Lyla was diagnosed at 9 months old with quadriplegic cerebral palsy.

Lyla started attending therapy and I realised that I wasn't going back to my old job any time soon. I worked for myself for a year but my thoughts were always on work and not on Lyla where they should have been.

Gradually I accepted that I couldn't give Lyla the attention she needed and continue running my own business. Three years ago we returned to Glasgow to be closer to our families. My husband works in England through the week and I am the kids' primary

"Maybe the most important job for me to have at this point in my life is to be Lyla and Blair's mum"

care giver. Lyla attends our local mainstream school with her brother so my focus and time is spent on working closely with her amazing school to make sure she is settled and learning, making sure she gets the rest she needs to last the day, remembering that we have to build a castle for homework or that tomorrow is dress down day.

After 6.5 years I have come to embrace my role as a stay at home mum and channel my creative itches into writing and helping with community and school projects. As my mum once told me, maybe the most important job for me to have at this point in my life is to be Lyla and Blair's mum. "

"Things They Do Not Tell You..

They don't say when your wee girl is getting out of hospital.

You only find out when she needs something they didn't give her.

They don't say why the appointed officials are unable to attend her first Tribunal.

You are called upon to speak in their stead. You don't get to say how that feels.

They don't say when Psychology or Family Therapy can be provided.

You know that the 'unmet need' has been acknowledged.

They don't say when she was readmitted under Section.

They don't say when she absconds. The police make this known to you at 2 a.m. when they knock on your door, looking for her.

You help them find her.

You learn to phone the ward when you can't get in touch with her.

They don't tell you about her admission to supported living.

Nor do they tell you how happy they are to rid themselves of this difficult individual, on

"You learn to phone the ward when you can't get in touch with her"

Christmas Eve in the rain. They don't tell your sister, your brother, your children, aunts, uncles, grandparents, friends or anyone who might care.

They don't tell you why it is your job to clean up her filthy flat. You do it because you love her.

You buy her clothes, food, furniture, appliances. They don't tell you about support available.

But you find out about Self-directed Support and you push for the big meeting.

They do not tell you why they cannot show up and lend their expertise in this.

And they do not tell the student they sent instead.

They carry on not telling you. You carry on reaching out. The police show up from time to time.

Is she alive or dead? They never said.

You used to have a child. Now you have lots of questions. "

Imran's Story

"I was a post office manager at the time, and I was just standing at work one day and the sight in one eye just went. No warning, no pain, no nothing. I finished my shift and thought it might get better. The next day I went to the hospital and they said my retina had detached. They don't know why it happened to this day.

I was going in for my third operation and I noticed a little speck in my other eye. They said that retina had detached as well. I asked when I could get back to driving and they said it's never going to happen. In the waiting room I just started crying. I wasn't prepared for it, I wasn't expecting it. I thought I would just go back to my old life. I went home and stayed in bed for two weeks.

Eventually I managed to pick myself up and went to the RNIB and they said they could help me find a job. I started volunteering and eventually a full-time job came up. Luckily, I got it. That came to an end and now I work for Access to Work. I go out and see people with sight loss, hearing loss and dyslexia to offer help, support and advice. I feel like I've come full circle. I'm helping

"I feel like I've come full circle. I'm helping people who were in my position"

people who were in my position.

The most amazing moment is when I'm seeing someone with sight loss and they see my white cane. Their mentality changes when they see somebody with sight loss doing this type of job. When I see the figures for people with disability in work it's heartbreaking. They just need a little bit of support.

It sounds weird to say, but losing my sight was one of the most positive experiences because now I'm helping people in a real way. Before that I was just plodding along rather than being in this great position. My confidence is sky high.

If you're facing sight loss and you are feeling really low, just know there is help and support out there. You have to reach out to people and, I assure you, they will reach back and help you."

43

"I never thought I would get out my bed again. The pain and fatigue were who I was now, or so I thought.

At a hospital appointment I was lucky to meet someone with the same condition. The man was an outdoor sports enthusiast. Me, a CAD Draughtsman. Both now unable to do what we loved. His advice, yes you are sick, however, you now have time. Time fraught with pain, anxiety, depression, yes but time to do what you want to do in life. His question to me, "What were you born to do?"

Me 'A writer, okay, a film director.'

I tell other folk with M.E. this same story.

One dark relentlessly unrestful night, I decided to take that person's advice, I

"I never thought I would get out my bed again. The pain and fatigue were who I was now, or so I thought"

got up and wrote a poem, it was called 'Don't trifle wae ma grannie.' I laughed for days afterwards, at the poem, and myself. I was very proud and happy, just for me. This poem, the first step to managing my disability in a better manner.

Due to the nature of the condition I have never seen that man again, nor do I know his name.

I have written around twenty poems, several songs and four plays. It keeps me well. "

" I have had hearing loss most of my life, it's impact on my ability to communicate increasing as the years went on. As a child I had enough hearing in one ear for the problem not to be noticeable.

When I started work as a young teacher, I became aware that I was struggling more and more to hear my pupils, to follow conversations in the staff room and to keep up with friends' chatter when out socialising. I needed support.

Hearing aids were not much help to me then, and even now my modern digital aids are only of limited support – I have gradually lost the ability to make out what folk are saying to me. I hear the voice, but I still struggle to understand the speech. I usually describe myself as 'deaf' or say I have a profound hearing loss so that people realise I am struggling to follow what they say.

Communication is so important, so being unable to hear tends to cut us

"I work so hard to hear all day long it becomes exhausting, I am always shattered, my self-esteem goes down"

off, it's isolating. I miss the jokes, the 'banter'; I miss the chatter and gossip most people take for granted; I miss a lot of family interaction. I work so hard to hear all day long it becomes exhausting, I am always shattered, my self-esteem goes down, my self-confidence plummets, I get frustrated and 'crabbit'! I often just hide away.

I found that there was a lot of support available out there from other people struggling with their hearing loss journey who would listen, could understand, could empathise and were willing to share their experiences. I am lucky to be part of a fantastic group of people who refuse to let their hearing loss define them. "

" I have a diagnosis of paranoid schizophrenia or so I am told. My heart doesn't accept this but my brain understands that the compulsory treatment I have had for the last ten years probably keeps me alive. Some of my life has been awful; the break-up of my marriage, the fact that I haven't seen my son for many years; those times in hospital, wanting to die; to rip myself to pieces. But despite this; much of my life has been wonderful. I am privileged to have worked for most of my life and currently work for the Mental Welfare Commission for Scotland; it is brilliant travelling round Scotland; meeting people with so many views and experiences.

The fact that I work part time is wonderful, it allowed me to finish my memoir START: a love story; a plea for forgiveness and a reflection on the natural world and loneliness. It also means that I can spend time with my partner, her young twins and Dash the dog, I love taking him for walks along the seashore listening to the curlews and oyster catchers.

There are so many assumptions about people like me; once I was told people

"There are so many assumptions about people like me; once I was told people like me should not be allowed to live!"

like me should not be allowed to live! But I have an MBE for services to mental health and helped with the creation of the current Mental Health Act and have spoken at the United Nations. In the past I set up many advocacy groups and helped challenge stigma. At one time I managed 7 staff at HUG (Action for Mental Health) and People First Highland.

In my twenties I spent time sailing the Atlantic and over coral reefs in the Far East. I have skied and walked in the hills, I have camped in the desert with my wife, two soldiers and two camels for company. I have walked in rain forests and I have been blessed with many amazing friends. I am incredibly lucky. Many people are less fortunate than me which makes me very sad. That needs to change. "

"I grew up in a scheme in the east end. It was quite poverty stricken. I noticed when my mum and dad split up, that's when I started rebelling. I had to grow up quicker than my years. We started with taking prescription drugs. When I was 15, I decided I was moving out of my mum's. I'd already tried heroin by then.

I don't remember a lot of those years. I got myself into a lot of tricky situations. I moved back in with my mum. Six months later I met my partner and he was a heroin addict and we started taking it now and again. Quickly I was using it every day then injecting it.

I kept all the outside looking good, my appearance was good. I was always scared to ask for help because I thought I would lose my kids. My partner introduced me to crack cocaine. That's when things went dark. I was using crack every single day for two years. It was horrible, it wasn't an existence, I was sleeping all day and up all night using. I'd been using drugs for 25 years.

It got to the point where I'd had enough. I met somebody from one of the recovery cafes and he said 'go down to our women's group and meet my partner, she's had the same

"I was at the point I was ready for help, I wanted recovery. I think I was ready for it"

experiences as you.' I was at the point I was ready for help, I wanted recovery. I think I was ready for it. I went down to the women's group and I walked in and I couldn't look at anybody. I didn't know how to communicate with people anymore. Everyone was dead welcoming. I loved it.

I started to volunteer. I jumped in head-first. The volunteering and getting friends, meeting people and hearing their stories, it gives you hope, your confidence starts building. My kids started smiling and they were like 'I'm so proud of you mum'. I done a song writing course and I wrote a song to my son, my 16 year old, telling him not to follow my footsteps.

My long-term goal is hopefully employment. But I'm still finding out who I am, I still don't know some of the stuff that I like. I thought really bad about myself for all they years and I've just started feeling good about myself and proud of myself. My life's turned 360, everything's falling into place. "

"Death to me is definitely a transition. It's the beginning of a new chapter. I'm an end of life doula and I support dying people to have the best death possible – but also to live life to the full before that.

It's about accompanying the dying person and their families and loved ones. That's the root of the word doula, a companion, or woman of service.

Sometimes simply holding somebody's hand and being in the moment with them is enough...there's something about human touch and connection. And that's a big part of the whole doula thing – nobody should have to die alone unless they choose to, whether they are at home, in a hospice or care home or prison, or in a hospital.

Doula work grows into so many other things - simply listening, making a lunch or doing dishes or going for walks. It could mean being with the dying person at the very end. But it's also the bit before that, the weeks and months, perhaps from the time of a terminal diagnosis or the withdrawal of treatment.

"I support dying people to have the best death possible – but also to live life to the full before that"

And doulas carry on looking after the person who has died after the death too, supporting the family to care for the body at home before the funeral if they would like to do that, making funeral arrangements, and sometimes conducting the funeral too.

My primary focus is really the practical, hands on care, the small but necessary daily tasks, and helping to make death and dying the ordinary, natural part of life that it actually is.

It feels important to me to be able to take away some of the fear around the whole process, and to encourage people to talk about it, to express what really matters to them, and to make sure they know all the options. I love the privilege of being with families at those times. We get to know each other well and it's lovely to form that relationship of trust and safety. "

" I was diagnosed with MS nearly 20 years ago and after a slow but relentless decline in mobility, I am now completely dependent on my wheelchair and mobility scooter to get about.

When I was first diagnosed and still walking well, I wanted to try and do something about my condition and one of the options available was Hyperbaric Oxygen. This treatment is to breathe pure oxygen while under pressure and after researching it, I decided to try the process.

I was feeling optimistic about its potential effectiveness and went for treatment in a nearby centre but when I got there, I got a terrible shock. It was busy, full of people in wheelchairs, with walking sticks, people completely dependent on carers, in fact with a whole range of issues I wasn't ready to see. It's not that I couldn't handle the fact I might become one of them, it's just that I wanted to get on with my life and didn't want to be reminded of possibilities in the future.

"On that first visit I was blind to everything but the range of disabilities I might have to face"

12 years later and after significant decline to my current state, I restarted the treatment and soon my weekly visits became a highlight of the week. The people there are still burdened by the range of problems I had first seen but now I also saw laughter, discussions about common issues, mutual support and above all an open and sympathetic friendship of fellow sufferers, carers and supporters.

On that first visit I was blind to everything but the range of disabilities I might have to face and never recognised the importance of contact with compassionate, positive thinking and above all, a caring group of people. I do now. "

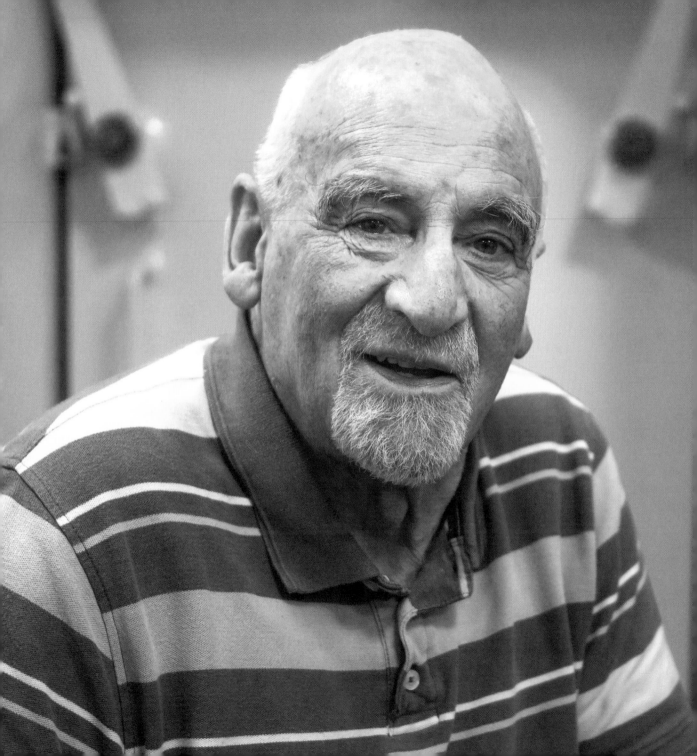

" I always felt different from everyone else: my hair, my skin, my height. Being mixed race, and an only child for ten years, I couldn't even see myself in my family members.

I did not see my differences as normal varieties of human life – I saw them as problems to fix. If this was not the way everyone else looked it must have been the wrong way. Instead of exploring and accepting these aspects of my being I tried to change them.

However, the only thing I could change was my weight. I believed that people wouldn't focus on my differences if I was super slim. I could use an eating disorder as armour.

I started controlling my food intake and purging after meals and this gave me a sense of security. I felt like I was doing something right. From that initial moment I turned to food restriction to give me a sense of control and release in times when I felt distress over things out of my control. Things like family issues, schoolwork and friendships. Later I used an eating disorder as a method of self-harm.

"I did not see my differences as normal varieties of human life – I saw them as problems to fix"

When I moved to high school my mental health became worse. I had become so hateful of myself that I believed I was not worthy of anything. When I became suicidal I realised I had to begin counseling where I learned that sometimes you cannot change things and that's ok. I could not fix everything and sometimes you just have to accept that and move on.

Leaving school and moving to university I was exposed to more diversity and finally met people who were more like me, inside and out. I began the journey of exploring my identity instead of trying to blend it out. I surrounded myself with people who I felt comfortable with and who uplifted me.

Seeing my peers enjoy life care-free helped me to understand that being different is not always bad and I have learned not to be so hateful to myself because I am the only one that is in control of my own happiness. "

" I have rheumatoid arthritis and was diagnosed at the age of 24. For me, the hardest part of my long term condition is that people can't see it, so assume I am perfectly healthy.

That security guard who told me (he didn't even ask, or check for a badge which I had) that I needed to move my car from the disabled parking space, couldn't see how fatigued I was feeling and just assumed I had parked there out of laziness. And he definitely couldn't see how his assumption made me feel even worse for the rest of the day. I had to justify myself in front of other people entering the building.

That coffee barista who told me the toilets were upstairs after I'd asked for the key for the accessible toilet downstairs, didn't know that I was in too much pain to walk up that flight of stairs, and that's why I was asking for the key. He just assumed I would be able to use the regular toilets because there was no visible sign of a disability, and completely ignored my request for a key. I had to explain my situation in front of a queue of customers.

"I've gotten used to the judgmental stares I get, but that doesn't make it any easier to deal with or make me feel less self conscious"

Sometimes I can use the stairs, sometimes I need a lift. Sometimes I can use a regular restroom but sometimes I need a bit more space and support to get back up. Sometimes I can manage to walk around the supermarket but not be able to walk across the car park on top of this.

I've gotten used to the judgmental stares I get, but that doesn't make it any easier to deal with or make me feel less self conscious. I just wish people wouldn't be so quick to jump to conclusions and assume that because you look fine, that you are fine. "

"My young cousin took his own life. He'd been suffering with poor mental health, but he was talking, he was talking to his mum and dad. He had a wide circle of friends and he was loved by everybody and he gave a lot of love, he was a really special guy.

I got a phone call, my sister phoned me and told me 'Grant's dead.' I'll never forget how I felt, and the family was collapsing around me. Four hundred people turned up at the funeral, it was really special. We had a tree with people writing memories of him, we had photographs of him - he used to go travelling round India, he was a bit of a dude and we shared stories about him, and it was beautiful. It was such a hard time.

I'd heard about this men's club, Andy's Man Club and a friend who comes from Oban had set one up and he said why don't you do one in Glasgow. It felt like the right time to do it. I thought if this is in anyway a legacy for Grant, for my cousin, to show that we're doing something, well I don't want anyone else to feel what we felt. If we could do something simple in Glasgow maybe some other men

"He had a wide circle of friends and he was loved by everybody... he was a really special guy"

could find there are actually options and wouldn't take their own life.

On the night 31 men turned up. It was amazing. It grew and it grew. It's true peer to peer support. We just let them talk. We stop for teas and coffees, that's when men who didn't know each other start talking. It's amazing to watch because we get men that come in with their heads between their legs, they can hardly look at you, really quite shy, absolutely worried about coming in the door.

We've gone our own way now, we're Mind the Men. I always feel very positive, seeing the transformation, we're seeing the guys' journeys. You're reassuring these men that they're not alone. They've now got a club that they're part of. That's 'Mind the Men'. "

"Manchester United was Frankie's first club that he played for professionally and the players who played under Sir Matt Busby wore the Busby Babe Blazer, which Frankie got when he was seventeen years old.

Fast forward to his courageous battle with dementia which began in 2008. He had lost his job, we both hadn't reached pension age, and I'd given up my work to care for him and we were struggling to pay the ordinary household bills and the personal care charges.

He said, 'what about my Man United blazer?' So, we found an avid Man United collector and we sold it to him.

We didn't get a lot of money for it, but got enough to help to pay the bills. It was quite heart wrenching letting it go.

It was one Tuesday in April 2014 and we knew that Frankie didn't have that long to live. A knock came to the door, our son Scott went to answer it. He came through to the bedroom and said, 'Mum, there's a big box in the kitchen for you and Dad.' Here was the blazer and the most beautiful note from the guy who had bought it, saying he wanted to gift it back to Frankie because he'd heard how seriously ill he was.

63

"Someday, Frankie and I will meet again where the angels learn to fly, and I know he'll be waiting for me. I've just got to be patient"

I remember putting it on a hanger, hanging it on the back of the door and saying to Frankie, 'your blazer's come home son, and when you waken up, you'll see it'. The following morning, he died at ten past six. I think he was just waiting for his blazer to come home.

Frank's Law was a campaign to extend free personal care to the under 65s in Scotland. We found through Frankie's journey, as he deteriorated and was assessed as needing help with personal care, he was charged for it, but if he were over 65 it was free.

It got me thinking how many other under 65s in Scotland weren't as lucky as us, they didn't have memorabilia they could sell to pay for that personal care. A lot of them were struggling paying for that personal care.

I so wish Frankie was here today to see how many people are going to be helped by the law that's now named after him and that his death was not in vain."

The Little White Rose

By Hugh MacDiarmid (To John Gawsworth)

The rose of all the world is not for me.

I want for my part

Only the little white rose of Scotland

That smells sharp and sweet—and breaks the heart.

About the ALLIANCE

The Health and Social Care Alliance Scotland (the ALLIANCE)'s vision is for a Scotland where people of all ages who are disabled or living with long term conditions, and unpaid carers, have a strong voice and enjoy their right to live well, as equal and active citizens, free from discrimination, with support and services that put them at the centre.

The ALLIANCE has three core aims; we seek to:

- Ensure people are at the centre, that their voices, expertise and rights drive policy and sit at the heart of design, delivery and improvement of support and services.

- Support transformational change, towards approaches that work with individual and community assets, helping people to stay well, supporting human rights, self management, co-production and independent living.

- Champion and support the third sector as a vital strategic and delivery partner and foster better cross-sector understanding and partnership.

www.alliance-scotland.org.uk

 @AllianceScot

 @alliance.scotland

 Health and Social Care Alliance Scotland

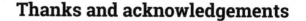
ALLIANCE
HEALTH AND SOCIAL CARE
ALLIANCE SCOTLAND
people at the centre

Thanks and acknowledgements

The ALLIANCE would like to express our gratitude to everyone who has shared their story as part of the Humans of Scotland series. Your contributions have created records of lived experience that are striking in their honesty. Thank you for your willingness, your openness and your generosity in sharing the details of your lives. A thank you also to those providing support and services for kindly liaising with us to spread the word on the project among those you work with. You put us in touch with remarkable people. We would like to acknowledge Steven McGregor for the book design and the vision of the photographers who have represented the participants of Humans of Scotland in such inspiring ways, namely Marc Millar Photography and others including Craig Chalmers, Fara West and Freya Macdonald. This project was carried out by the Humans of Scotland team, Alison Livingstone, Angela Millar and Justine Duncan.

The ALLIANCE is a company registered by guarantee. Registered in Scotland No. 307731 Charity number SC037475

Registered office, Venlaw Building, 349 Bath Street, Glasgow, G2 4AA

This publication featured original copy based on the ALLIANCE's Humans of Scotland project.

All photos featured have been taken by the ALLIANCE, professional photographer or Humans of Scotland contributors.

The publication is not for sale or resale and has not been produced for any commercial purpose.

Animal Young

Fish

Rod Theodorou

Heinemann
LIBRARY

First published in Great Britain by
Heinemann Library,
Halley Court, Jordan Hill, Oxford OX2 8EJ
a division of Reed Educational and Professional
Publishing Ltd.
Heinemann is a registered trademark of Reed
Educational & Professional Publishing Ltd.

OXFORD MELBOURNE AUCKLAND
JOHANNESBURG BLANTYRE GABORONE
IBADAN PORTSMOUTH (NH) USA CHICAGO

Designed by Celia Floyd
Illustrations by Alan Fraser
Printed in Hong Kong/China

03 02 01 00 99
10 9 8 7 6 5 4 3 2 1

ISBN 0 431 03080 4

British Library Cataloguing in Publication Data

Theodorou, Rod
  Fish. – (Animal young)
  1. Fishes – Infancy – Juvenile literature
  I. Title
  597.1'39

Acknowledgements
The Publishers would like to thank the following for
permission to reproduce photographs:

Ardea London Ltd p. 13; BBC: Jeff Foott p. 15; Bruce
Coleman: Pacific Stock p. 7, Charles & Sandra Hood
p. 16, Jane Burton pp. 17, 22; FLPA: Steve
McCutcheon p. 9; NHPA: Norbert Wu p. 12; OSF:
Keith Ringland p. 6, David Thompson p. 8, David B
Fleetham p. 10, Zig Leszczynski p. 11, Mark Deeble &
Victoria Stone p. 14, Rudie Kuiter p. 20, Peter Parks
p. 23, Jeff Foott p. 24, Rodger Jackman p. 25; Planet
Earth: Peter Scoones p. 21; Tony Stone: Fred
Bavendam p. 5, Marc Chamberlain p. 19.

Cover photograph reproduced with permission of
Oxford Scientific Films/
M. Deeble/V. Stone

Any words appearing in the text in bold, **like this**,
are explained in the Glossary.

Contents

Introduction

There are many different kinds of animals. All animals have babies. They look after their babies in different ways.

These are the six main animal groups.

Mammal Bird Reptile

Amphibian Fish Insect

This book is about fish. Fish live in ponds, lakes, rivers and seas all over the world. There are lots of different kinds of fish.

The whale shark is the biggest fish in the world.

What is a fish?

All fish:

- live in water
- breathe **oxygen** with their **gills**
- swim using their **fins**.

Salmon

fins

gills under
gill cover

scales

tail fin

Most fish:

- have hard **scales** on their body
- lay eggs that **hatch** into baby fish.

Eels are fish but most do not have scales.
Their bodies are soft and smooth.

Making a nest

Most fish do not make nests. They lay their eggs in the water and swim away. Some fish make a nest for their eggs. The nest keeps the eggs safe.

Sticklebacks make a little cave out of weeds on the **river-bed**.

Fish make their nests at the bottom of rivers or at the **sea-bed**. They scoop out a hole in the sand with their bodies. Some even push weeds into their nests.

This female salmon digs a nest and then covers her eggs with gravel to keep them safe.

Protecting the nest

Some fish stay close to their nests and guard their eggs or baby fish from **predators**. They attack any other animal that comes near the nest.

This triggerfish will attack anything that comes near his eggs – even divers!

Eggs are laid by female fish, but it is often the male fish that looks after them. He may go for days without food just to protect the eggs.

When the 2-metre-long male African lungfish is protecting his nest, other fish stay away!

Eggs

Most fish lay thousands, or even millions of eggs. The eggs are usually tiny and round. They do not have hard shells and are easily eaten by other animals.

When this ocean sunfish grows up it will be able to lay over 5 million eggs at once!

Other fish lay hard egg cases shaped like a purse. They have a curly leg at each corner that hooks onto seaweed. The eggs stay there until the babies **hatch**.

This baby dogfish shark grows inside an egg case.

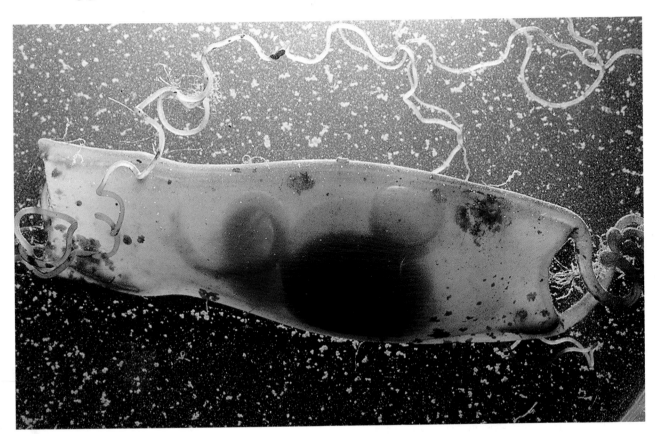

Fish fry

When baby fish **hatch** from eggs they are called **fry** or larva. They are often tiny; only a few millimetres long. They do not look much like their parents yet.

Tiny fish fry like these emperor cichlid fry are very hard for **predators** to spot.

Some fry have a bag growing under their stomachs called a **yolk sac**. The fry do not need to go hunting. They can live for weeks off the food in their yolk sacs.

This salmon fry stays hidden in gravel for weeks, living off its yolk sac.

Staying safe

When millions of fish eggs **hatch** into millions of fish **fry**, they attract lots of **predators**. Other fish, shrimps, crabs, and jellyfish eat huge numbers of fry.

This Dover sole has attacked a fish fry.

Fish fry try to stay hidden from predators.
Some hide at the **sea-bed** amongst rocks or weeds.
Others swim next to floating weeds or wood at
the surface.

These red devil fry are hiding among rocks
on the sea-bed.

Live birth

Some sharks and other fish do not lay eggs.
Their babies grow inside them and are born alive.
The babies are born strong and ready to catch
their own food.

A nurse shark baby would look exactly like
its mother.

Fish that give birth to live young only have a few babies at a time. Their babies are much harder for **predators** to catch and eat than tiny fish **fry**.

Stingrays give birth to live young.

Looking after the young

Most fish do not look after their young. A few kinds of fish do stay close to their young and protect them.

Male seahorses have a special **pouch** where the female lays her eggs. The young **hatch** out from the pouch and dash back inside if they are in danger.

Some kinds of fish look after their **fry** in their mouths! They suck up their eggs and fry and keep them safe in their mouths.

If they are in danger these cichlid fry swim into their mothers' mouth.

Growing up

As fish **fry** grow up their **yolk sacs** disappear and they have to find their own food. They feed on **plankton** and other tiny water creatures.

These jewel cichlid fry are looking for food on the **sea-bed**.

A shoal of
young fry
on the Great
Barrier Reef.

Young fish often swim together in large groups
called shoals or schools. They are safer in a shoal.
When a big fish attacks a shoal it cannot decide
which fish to chase.

23

Amazing journeys

Some fish do not spend all their lives in the same place. Instead they **migrate** huge distances.

Salmon **fry hatch** in rivers where they live for two years. Then they swim down to the sea. When they are older they swim back up the river to **breed**.

Migrating fish may take two or three years to reach the sea or river where they breed. Once they have laid their eggs they usually die.

These young eels swim across the ocean to live in rivers. Years later they swim back to the sea to breed.

How they grow

This is how a baby nurse shark is born.
The baby shark looks a lot like its mother.

Growth of a grey nurse shark

1 The baby shark
grows inside its
mother.

2 The baby is born live.

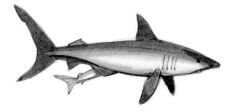

3 The baby swims off to
find its own food.

This is how a sole (called a flatfish) **hatches** and grows up. The sole **fry** does not look much like its mother.

Growth of a European sole

1 The adult female lays about half a million eggs.

2 Tiny fish fry hatch out of the eggs. Their bodies are not flat like their mother.

3 Soon the fry starts to look more like its mother. The body becomes flatter. One eye moves from one side of the head to the other side.

4 After six weeks the fry looks like its mother.

Fish and other animals

		Fish
What they look like:	Bones inside body	all
	Number of legs	none
	Hair on body	none
	Scaly skin	most
	Wings	none
	Feathers	none
Where they live:	Lives on land	none
	Lives in water	all
How they are born:	Grows babies inside body	some
	Lays eggs	most
How they feed young:	Feeds baby milk	none
	Bring babies food	none

Amphibians	Insects	Reptiles	Birds	Mammals
all	none	all	all	all
4 or none	6	4 or none	2	2 or 4
none	all	none	none	all
none	none	all	none	few
none	most	none	all	some
none	none	none	all	none
most	most	most	all	most
some	some	some	none	some
few	some	some	none	most
most	most	most	all	few
none	none	none	none	all
none	none	none	most	most

Glossary

breed   a male and a female come together to make babies

fin   flat part of a fish's body that helps it to swim or turn

fry   very small, young fish

gill   part of a fish's body that takes oxygen from water to help it breathe

hatch   to be born from an egg

migrate   to move from one place to another each year

oxygen   a gas that all animals and plants need to breathe in order to live

plankton   tiny animals and plants that live in the sea

pouch   pocket of skin on the stomach of some animals in which their babies grow

predator   an animal that hunts and kills other animals for food

river-bed   the ground at the bottom of a river

scales   small, flat, pieces of hard skin that cover a fish's body

sea-bed   the ground at the bottom of the sea

yolk sac   a bag of food that is part of some baby fish and which they can eat after they are born

Further reading

Dolphin, Claire Robinson, *Really Wild*, Heinemann Library, 1999.

Fish, Steve Parker, *Eyewitness Guides*, Dorling Kindersley, 1990.

Inside a Coral Reef, Carole Telford and Rod Theodorou, *Amazing Journeys*, Heinemann Library, 1997.

Pond and River, Steve Parker, *Eyewitness Guides*, Dorling Kindersley, 1988.

Shark, Claire Robinson, *Really Wild*, Heinemann Library, 1999.

Shark and Dolphin, Carole Telford and Rod Theodorou, *Spot the Difference* , Heinemann Library, 1996.

The Dorling Kindersley Big Book of Knowledge, Dorling Kindersley, 1994.

The Usborne Book of World Wildlife, Usborne, 1994.

Index